To the Finish Line!

 Counting in order, draw a line from **0** to **10**

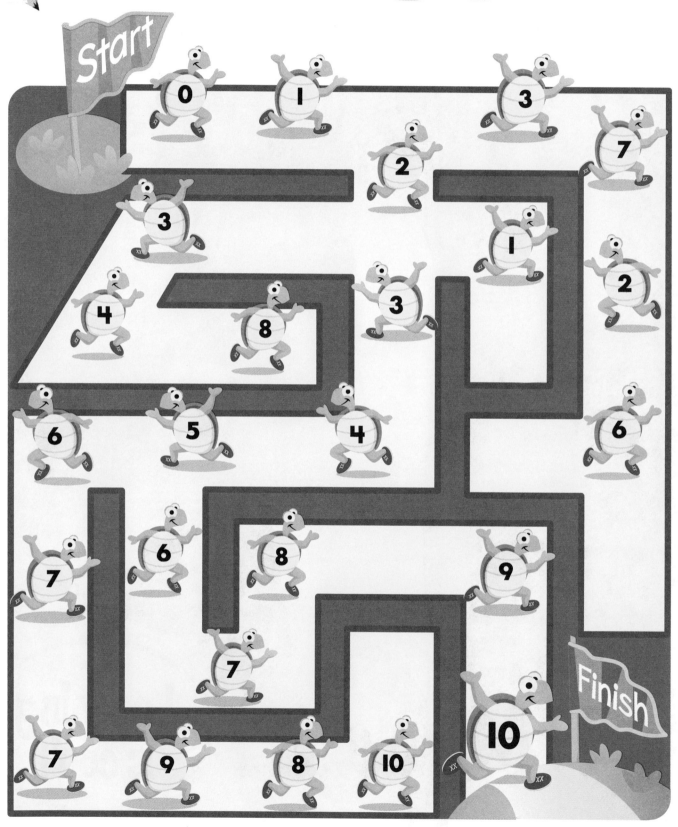

Egg Race

Circle 11 spoons

Color 20 hens

Color 13 eggs

EGG RACE

Count Numbers 11 to 20

Which Place?

Circle who won the race.

Circle who came in 2nd.

Circle who came in 3rd.

FUN fact! Wow! Rusty Harrison won the World's 1st International Bathtub Race.

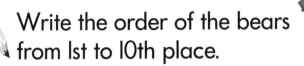 # In the First Place

 Write the order of the bears from 1st to 10th place.

Color the bear in 2nd place

Color the bear in 5th place

Color the bear in 7th place

FUN TO DO!

Have a race with two friends. See who comes in 1st, 2nd, and 3rd place.

Sack Race

Finish Line

Which animal is in 1st place? Write the number.

Which animal is in 2nd place? Write the number.

Which animal is in 3rd place? Write the number.

Which animal is in 4th place? Write the number.

Animal Games

Write the answer in each box.

How many 🐰 are on the ⬭ ? ____

How many 🐱 are playing ⬬ ? ____

How many 🐘 are on the ⬭ ? ____

How many 🐢 are at the ⬭ ? ____

Review Numbers 0–12

Turtle Cove Treasure

Paddy found a treasure map. Paddy takes 2 steps forward, 5 steps forward, and 4 steps forward to look for the treasure. Count his steps on the number line.

What number is the treasure near?

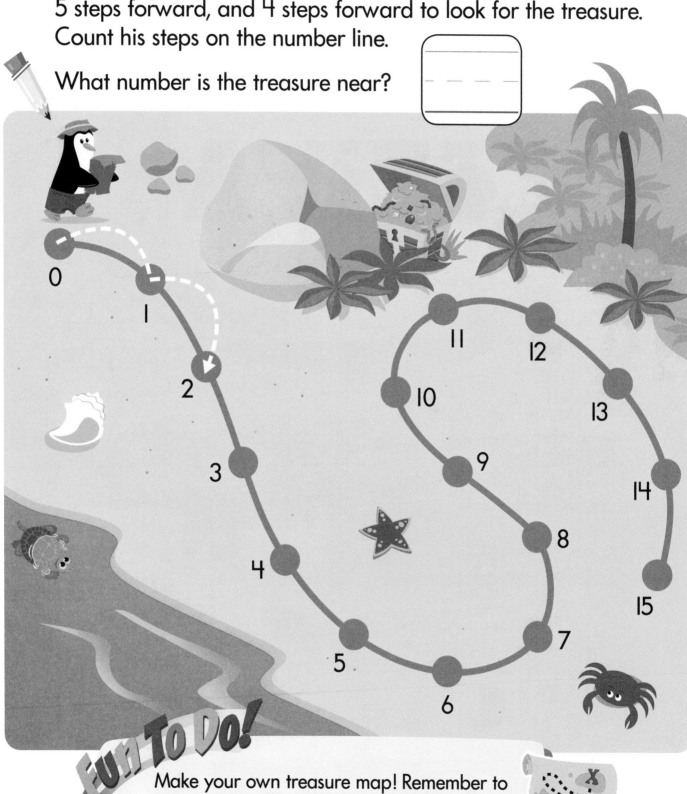

Fun To Do!

Make your own treasure map! Remember to hide your treasure. See if a friend can find it.

Count the penguins to complete the story.

[___] penguins are hunting for treasure.

[___] more penguins join the hunt.

How many penguins are hunting for treasure?

$3 + 8 =$ [___]

You're JOKING!

If I have 25 apples in one hand and 10 apples in my other hand, what do I have?

Very big hands!

Learn Addition

Step by Step

Find more treasure! Count on the number line. Paddy goes 2 steps forward, 5 steps forward, and 7 steps forward to the boathouse.

What number is the boathouse near?

How Many?

 Add the coins 🪙 emeralds 💎 and rubies 🔴
Write the number sentence in the box.

 **Peter Penguin has**

4 coins 🪙
1 emerald 💎
1 ruby 🔴

How many things are in Peter's sack?

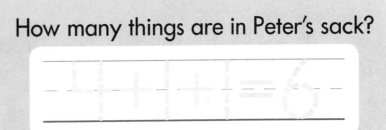

$4 + 1 + 1 = 6$

 **Penny Penguin has**

3 coins 🪙
2 emeralds 💎
4 rubies 🔴

How many things are in Penny's sack?

 **Paul Penguin has**

2 coins 🪙
5 emeralds 💎
5 rubies 🔴

How many things are in Paul's sack?

 **Paddy Penguin has**

7 coins 🪙
2 emeralds 💎
4 rubies 🔴

How many things are in Paddy's sack?

Add Three Numbers

Paddy's Lost Treasure

 Write numbers to complete the story.

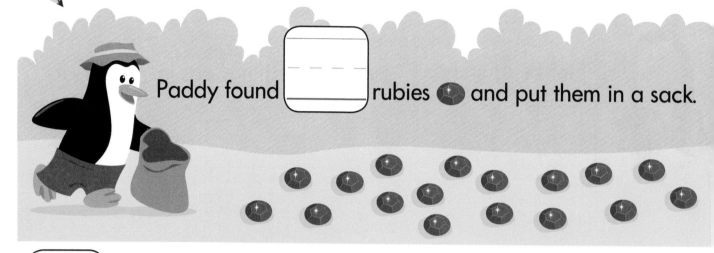

Paddy found _____ rubies and put them in a sack.

_____ rubies fell out of his sack on the way back to camp.

How many rubies did Paddy have left?

$$17 - 8 = \boxed{}$$

Back to the Camp

Paddy goes 5 steps and then 1 step to the tent.

Count on the number line. What number is in front of the tent?

Yummy Soup

Paddy and his penguin pals are hungry!

Paddy eats 3 bowls of soup. Color 3 bowls ■
Penny eats 2 bowls of soup. Color 2 bowls ■
Peter eats 5 bowls of soup. Color 5 bowls ■

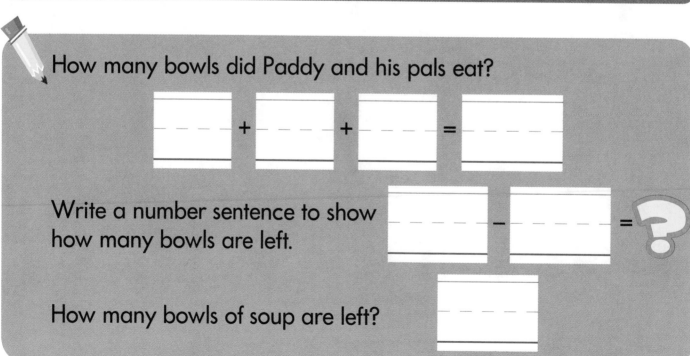

How many bowls did Paddy and his pals eat?

☐ + ☐ + ☐ = ☐

Write a number sentence to show how many bowls are left.

☐ − ☐ = ?

How many bowls of soup are left?

☐

Shipping Out

Paddy Penguin is looking for treasure! He wants to bring it back to the ship. Paddy goes 8 steps forward and 2 steps back. He then goes 9 steps forward.

The treasure is at 6.

Did Paddy stop at the treasure? _____

What number did Paddy finish on? _____

Did Paddy make it back to the ship? _____

Places in the Pond

Follow the directions. Circle each answer.

Find number 11. Count ahead 6 lily pads.
Find number 30. Count back 5 lily pads.
Find number 34. Count ahead 7 lily pads.
Find number 38. Count back 4 lily pads.

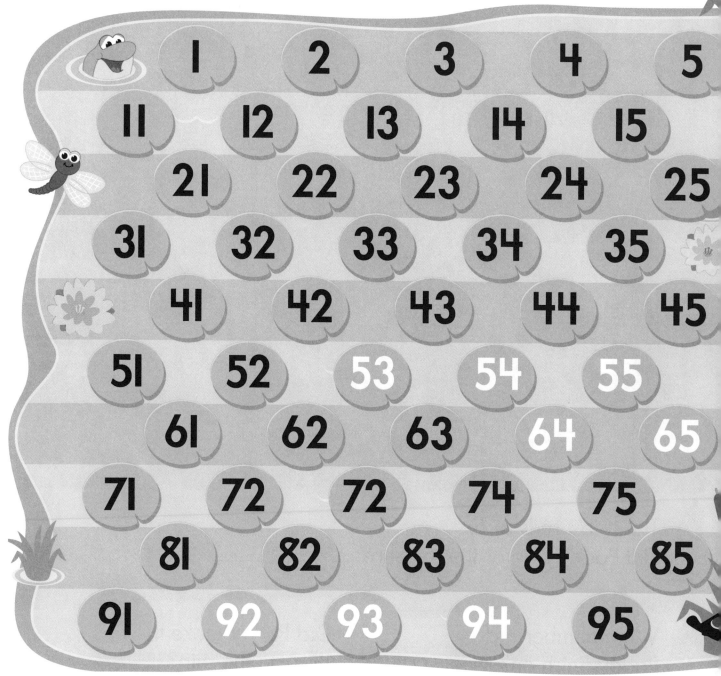

1	2	3	4	5
11	12	13	14	15
21	22	23	24	25
31	32	33	34	35
41	42	43	44	45
51	52	53	54	55
61	62	63	64	65
71	72	72	74	75
81	82	83	84	85
91	92	93	94	95

Color the number that is:

3 more than 63 ▢
7 less than 77 ▢
8 more than 84 ▢

6	7	8	9	10
16	17	18	19	20
26	27	28	29	30
36	37	38	39	40
46	47	48	49	50
56	57	58	59	60
66	67	68	69	70
76	77	78	79	80
86	87	88	89	90
96	97	98	99	100

Learn and Understand 1–100

Creepy Crawly Count

Match each number to a picture.

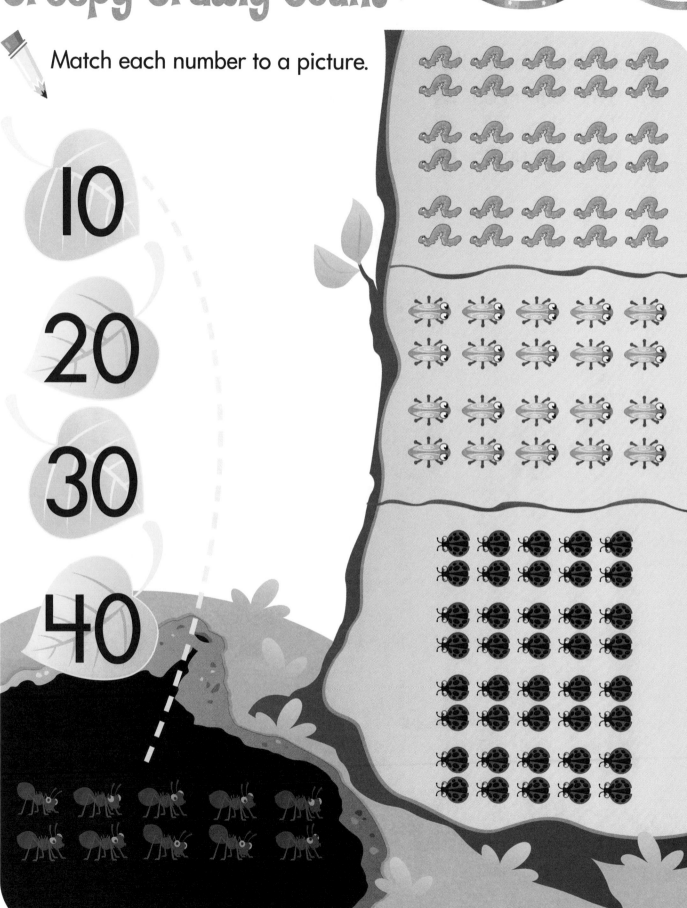

10

20

30

40

Let's Get Hatching!

Color the white eggs.

Write the number of eggs in each carton.

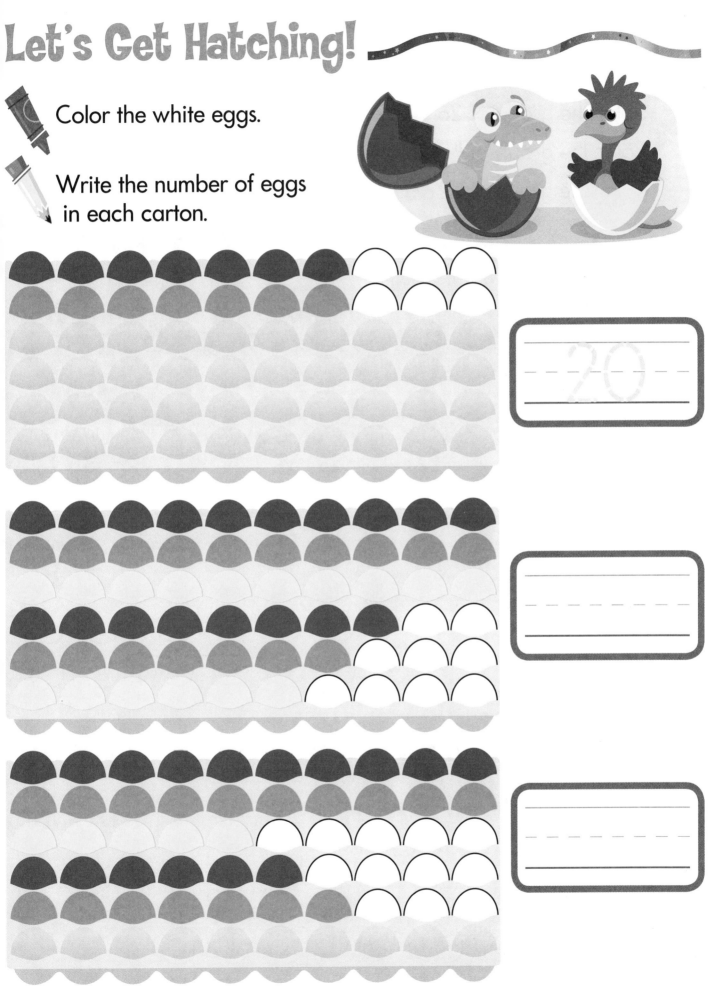

20

Koala Count

Color the group of 26 █

Color the group of 14 █

Color the group of 32 ░

tens	ones

tens	ones

tens	ones

Kangaroo-dle Doodle

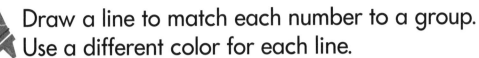

Draw a line to match each number to a group.
Use a different color for each line.

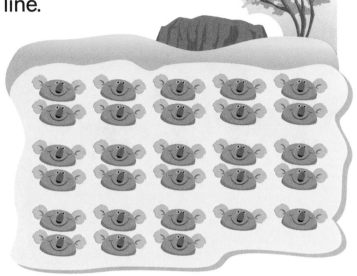

Read Numbers as Tens and Ones

Ones and Tens

Write numbers to complete the number story.

There are _____ red dingoes.

There are _____ brown dingoes.

_____ blue dingoes also come to the waterhole.

How many dingoes are there in all? _____

Emu Express

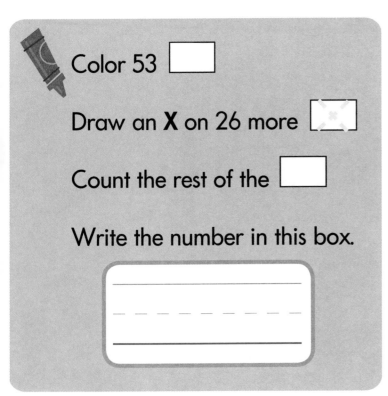

Color 53 ☐

Draw an **X** on 26 more ☒

Count the rest of the ☐

Write the number in this box.

23

Review Numbers up to 100

Skills with Bills

 Draw a line to match each bag
to a money amount.

$15

$30

$23

$7

$20
$10

$5
$1 $1

$10
$5

$1
$10 $1
$10 $1

It All Adds Up

 Welcome to Fair Fields Bank. Add the money. Write your answer in the box.

$ _____ . ____ 00

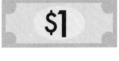
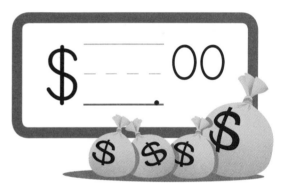

$ _____ . ____ 00

$ _____ . ____ 00

$ _____ . ____ 00

Fun Finds

 Match each price tag to the coins that match.

   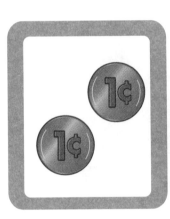

 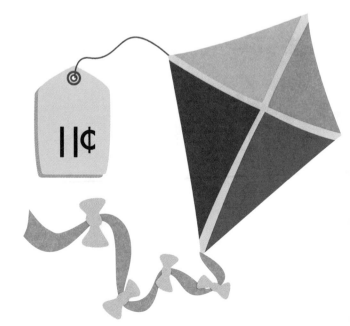

On the Money Train

Add the coins. Write
the answer in the box.

¢

¢

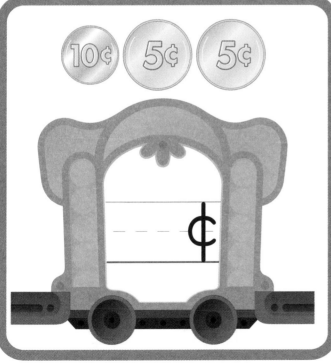

¢

¢

Add Money

A Penny Saved

Write numbers to complete the number story.

Carrie has _____ ¢.

Carrie gets _____ ¢ for doing chores.

Carrie finds _____ ¢ under the bed.

How much money does Carrie have now? $ _____

Wealthy Wagon

Draw a line to help the Otters get to Fair Fields.

Keep track of the money the Otters find. Mark it on the grid.

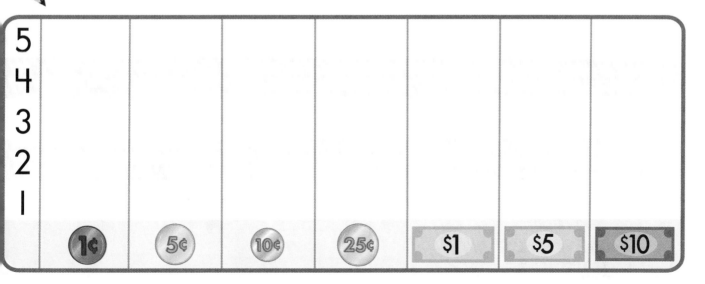

Carnival Corner

 How many **circles** ● do you see?

How many **triangles** ▲ do you see?

Here Comes a Parade

Circle each **rectangle**.
Write the total in the box.

Draw a triangle around each **square**.
Write the total in the box.

rectangle

square

Identify Rectangles and Squares

The Fun Shape Band

Color the ▲
Color the ▲
Color the ●
Color the ■
Color the ▬

How many ▲ do you see? _____

How many ▲ do you see? _____

How many ● do you see? _____

How many ■ do you see? _____

How many ▬ do you see? _____

33 Identify Triangles, Circles, Squares, and Rectangles

Carnival Goodies

 Complete the other half to match. Then, color the picture.

Match-a-Mask

Circle the picture that completes each mask.

35 Identify Circles, Triangles, Squares, and Rectangles

Before the Parade

 Color the shapes in the picture using this code.

square   rectangle   triangle   circle

Crowning Around

Draw the shapes to complete each crown.

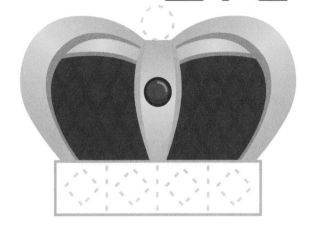

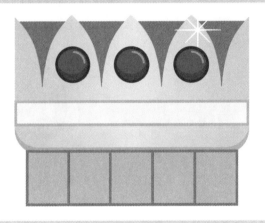
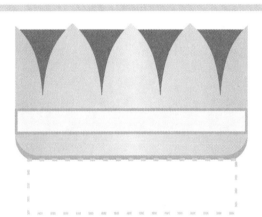

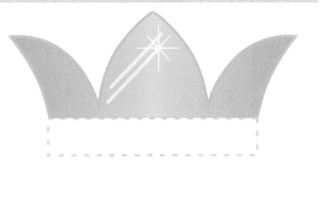

Fun To Do!

Make a crown with colored paper, gift wrap, glue, and a scissors! Cut and glue strips of paper to fit around your head. Decorate with shapes.

Shape Sorting

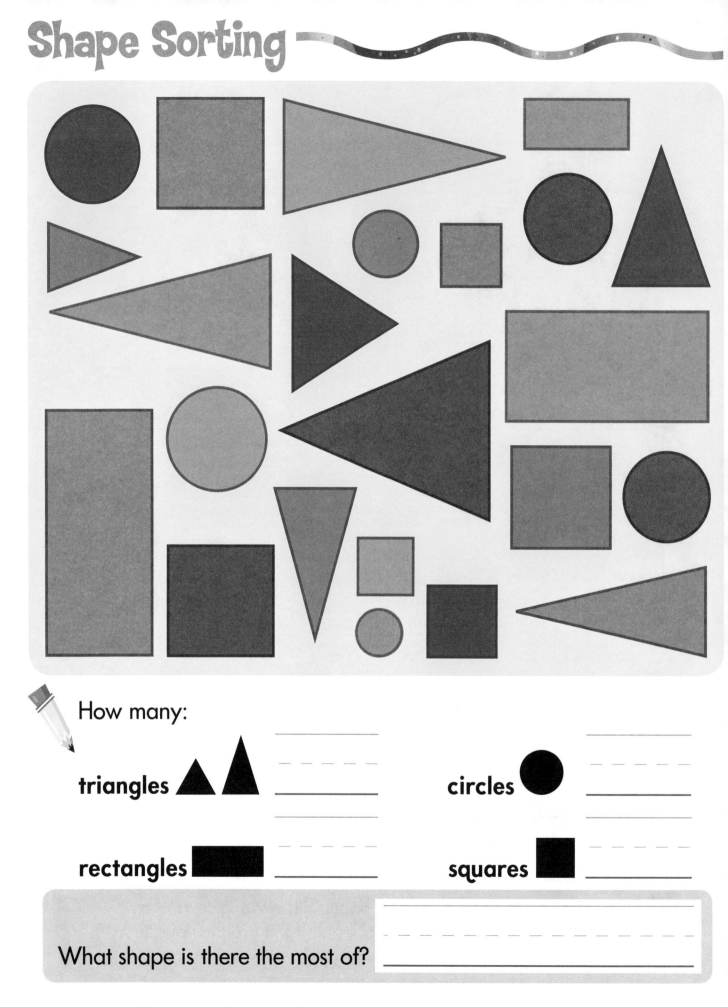

How many:

triangles ▲▲ _____

circles ● _____

rectangles ▬ _____

squares ■ _____

What shape is there the most of? _____

©TREND enterprises, Inc.

 Draw an **X** over the shape that is not used.

Review Complex Shapes

Robot World

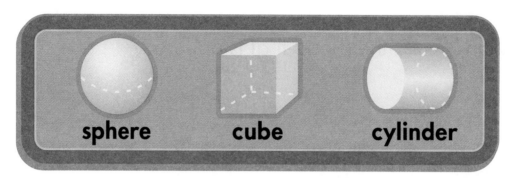

| sphere | cube | cylinder |

 Color each: **sphere** **cube** **cylinder**

Then, color the picture.

Recognize Spheres, Cubes, and Cylinders   40

Heavy Lifting

✏️ Trace each shape. Then, complete each unfinished shape.

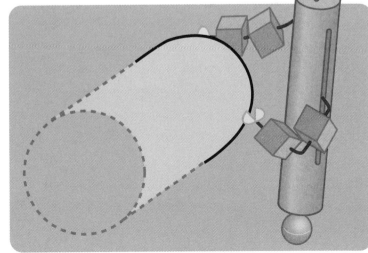

41

Draw Spheres, Cubes, and Cylinders

Robots Take a Break

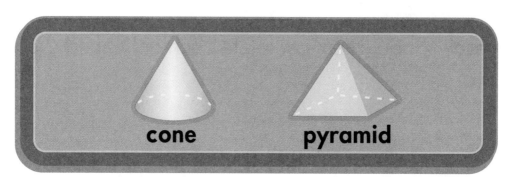

cone   pyramid

 Color each: **cone**   **pyramid**

Then, color the picture.

Robot Round-up

Trace each shape. Then, complete each unfinished shape.

Fun To Do!

Use 3-D shapes to draw your own farm animals. What shape did you use the most?

43

Draw Cones and Pyramids

Factory Fun

Color each: **sphere** **cube** **cylinder**

cone **pyramid** Then, color the picture.

Robot Races

 Circle each answer.

What shape is the: **red** robot?

orange robot?

purple robot?

blue robot?

green robot?

Review 3-D Shapes

Cover Me!

Circle the towel that can cover up each spill

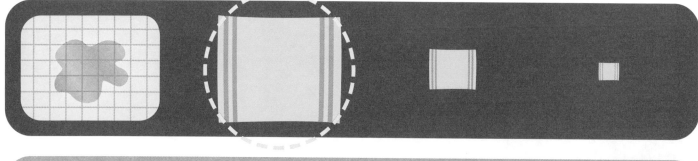

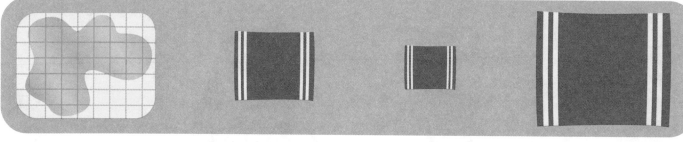

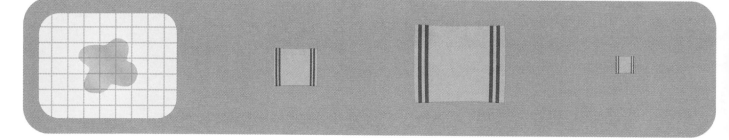

Just a Bit Longer

Draw each object from the locker above in order
from **shortest** to **longest**.

47

Order Length

Weight for Me!

Circle the picture that **weighs** more.

About Me:

This book belongs to me!

_____

I am

[   ]

years old.

Things I like to do

Me and my family.

Welcome, Parents!

Here's how to help your child have a successful learning experience:
- Find a quiet, comfortable place to work.
- Allow your child to set the pace.
- Offer plenty of praise and support.
- While the activities are designed so your child can work independently, there is an added benefit in working together.
- Take the time to talk and laugh. Enjoy being together!

TREND for KIDs

SKILLBOOK

GRADE

Add & Subtract

Numbers 0-100

Money & Time

Graphs & Charts

Zaner-Bloser® Writing Style

7+3=

4

2

4 - 2 =

Aligns with Learning Standards

Hours of learning FUN!®

Measuring Up

area

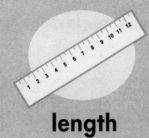

length

weight

 Match each picture to how it is measured.

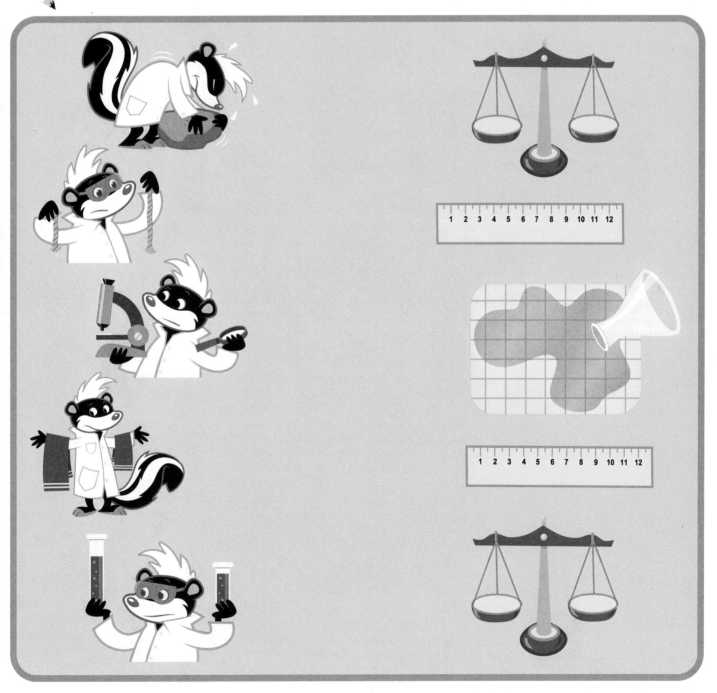

Apple Pick-Me-Up

Mazey Squirrel went apple picking. Read the graph to see how many apples she picked.

	Red Apples	Green Apples	Yellow Apples	Golden Apples
8	🍎			
7	🍎			
6	🍎		🍏	
5	🍎		🍏	
4	🍎		🍏	🍏
3	🍎	🍏	🍏	🍏
2	🍎	🍏	🍏	🍏
1	🍎	🍏	🍏	🍏

Write the number in the box.

How many 🍎 did Mazey pick? [ ]

How many 🍏 did Mazey pick? [ ]

How many 🍏 did Mazey pick? [ ]

How many 🍏 did Mazey pick? [ ]

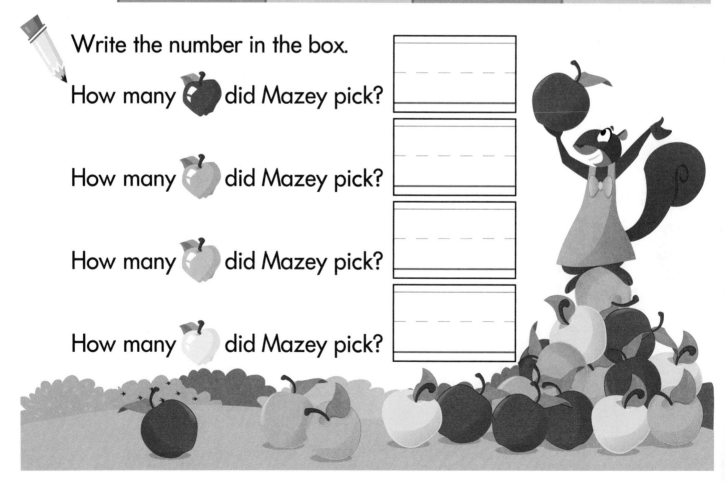

Read a Pictograph

50

Sweet Treats

Write how many
of each candy.

Draw pictures to complete the graph.

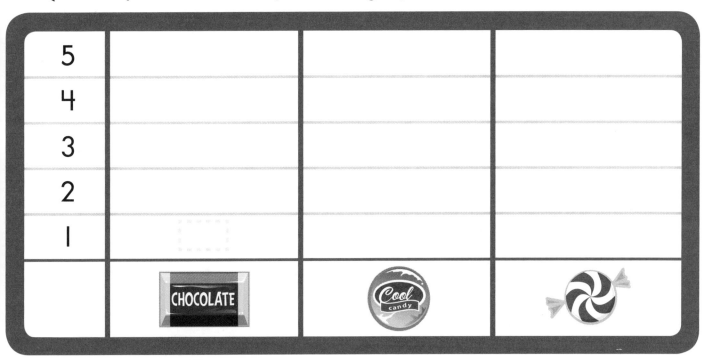

Empty your piggy bank. Count the coins and make the
graph on a sheet of paper. It may help to make stacks
of 5 coins. Which coin do you have the most of?

Costume Party

Mr. Smith's class has a fall party. Read the graph to see what costumes they wear.

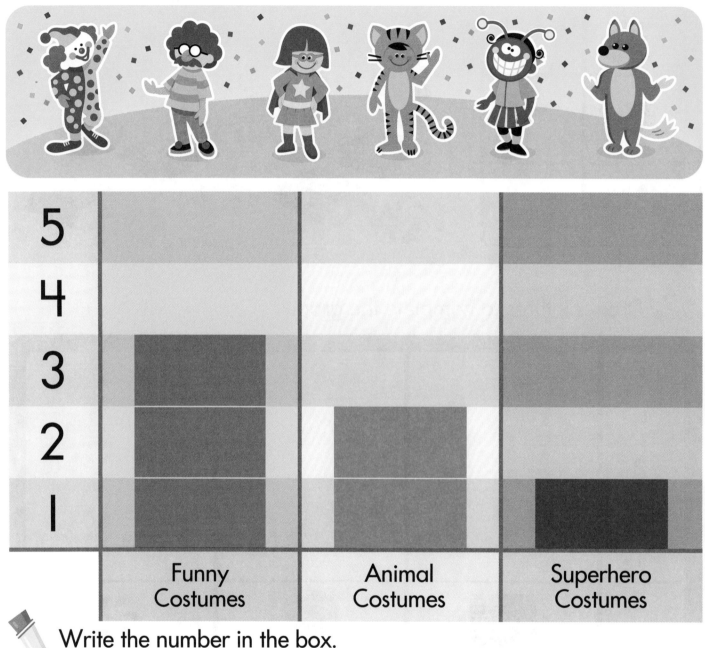

Write the number in the box.

How many funny costumes are there?	How many animal costumes are there?	How many superhero costumes are there?

Giving Thanks

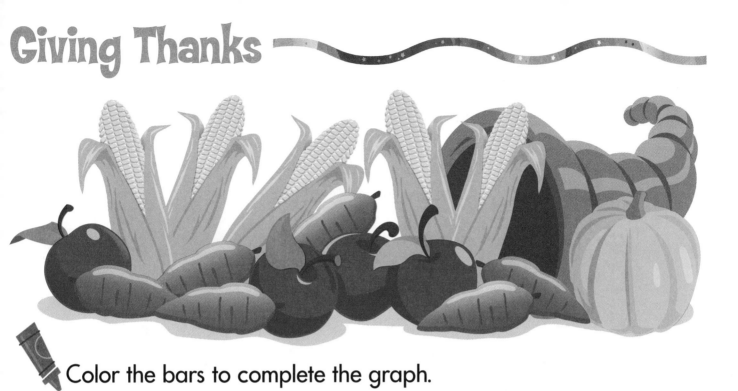

Color the bars to complete the graph.

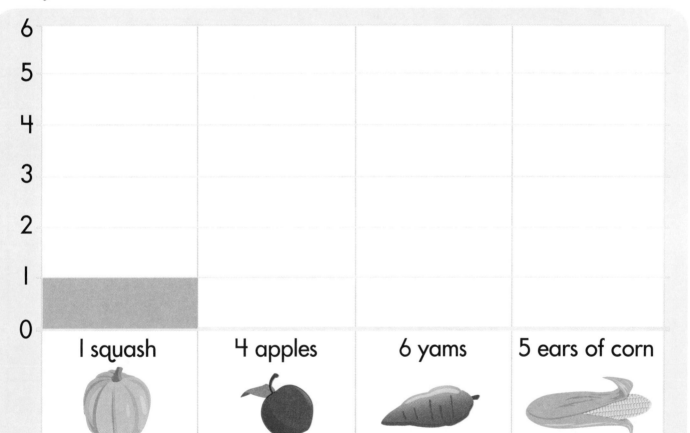

| | 1 squash | 4 apples | 6 yams | 5 ears of corn |

 Which food has the highest bar on your graph?

Miguel's May

Read each sentence. Circle the answer.

The last day of May is on what day?

Sunday   **Monday**   **Saturday**

How many days in one week?

4   5   7

Which day of the week comes before Thursday?

Friday   **Wednesday**   **Saturday**

How many days did Miguel walk his dog?

4   6   8

The first day of May is on what day?

Wednesday   **Friday**   **Thursday**

How many full weeks in May?

2   4   6

Sunday
4
11
18
25

May

Monday	Tuesday	Wednesday	Thursday	Friday	Saturday
			1	2	3
5	6	7	8	9	10
12	13	14	15	16	17
19	20	21	22	23	24
26	27	28	29	30	31

Read a Monthly Calendar

A Year at a Glance

Read each sentence. Circle the answer.

How many months are there in one year?

6   12   9

What month begins the new year?

December   June   January

What month comes after January?

February   March   December

What month comes before May?

June   March   April

How many days are there in the month of June?

29   30   31

How many days does Eric have guitar lessons?

2   4   1

January	February	March	April	May	June	July

June

Sunday	Monday	Tuesday	Wednesday	Thursday	Friday	Saturday
			1	2	3	4
5	6	7	8	9	10	11
12	13	14	15	16	17	18
19	20	21	22	23	24	25
26	27	28	29	30		

How many days are there in the month of October?

| 29 | 30 | 31 |

On what day of the month does vacation begin?

| 8th | 6th | 10th |

| August | September | October | November | December |

October

Sunday	Monday	Tuesday	Wednesday	Thursday	Friday	Saturday
	1	2	3	4	5	6
7	8	9	10 ✈	11	12	13
14	15	16	17	18	19	20
21	22	23	24	25	26	27
28	29	30	31			

Look at the Time!

Write the times to finish the story.
Then, draw the missing hand on each clock to show the time.

I eat my breakfast at _____ o'clock.

I get home from school at _____ o'clock.

I go to sleep at _____ o'clock.

Telling Time

 Match the clocks that show the same time.

Tell Time to Half-Hours

Anchors Away!

All aboard! Lee and her family are going on a cruise. Write the times to finish the story. Then, draw the missing hands on each clock to show the time.

The ship casts off at 7:30

The pool party is at 2:30

The costume party is at 6:00

Hints for Adults:
Beyond the Page!™

Shipping Out

Paddy Penguin is looking for treasure! He wants to bring it back to the ship. Paddy goes 8 steps forward and 2 steps back. He then goes 9 steps forward.

Finish
15
14
13
12
11
10
9
8
7
6
5
4
3
2
1
Start 0

✏ The treasure is at 6. Did Paddy stop at the treasure? _____

✏ What number did Paddy finish on? _____

Did Paddy make it back to the ship? _____

15

Review Addition and Subtraction

©TREND enterprises, Inc.

From everyday events to field trips, there are opportunities for learning all around you. Use these idea starters to involve your child in active learning fun **Beyond the Pages** of this skillbook . . . or create ideas of your own. These hints are great for:

- 🌀 **Building confidence**

- 🌀 **Engaging curiosity and imagination**

- 🌀 **Encouraging observation**

- 🌀 **Developing critical thinking**

- 🌀 **Opening a world of possibilities**

Treasure Hunt!

Use page 15 as your idea launch pad. Then, look at other pages in this skillbook to begin more **Beyond the Pages** learning adventures. Enjoy the journey!

- 🌀 Time for a tasty treasure. Create a map from your room to where a treat is hidden. Invite a friend or family member to use your map, and follow the clues to find the treat!

- 🌀 Hop! Skip! Jump! Decide where to go. Then skip and count the skips. Next, jump and count the jumps. Compare the difference.

- 🌀 Be a coin collector. Count how many each you have of pennies, nickels, dimes, and quarters.

Energize learning for the children in your life!

Answers

Page 2

Page 3

Page 4
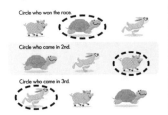

Page 5

Page 6

Finish Line
16 3 8 11

Page 7
Write 6, 12, 0, 3.

Page 8
Addition answer is 11.

Page 9
Addition answers are 3, 8, 11.

Page 10
Addition answer is 14.

Page 11
Row 1: 4 + 1 + 1 = 6;
Row 2: 3 + 2 + 4 = 9;
Row 3: 2 + 5 + 5 = 12;
Row 4: 7 + 2 + 4 = 13.

Page 12
Subtraction answers are 17, 8, 9.

Page 13
Subtraction answer is 9.

Page 14
 2, 3, 5.

3 + 2 + 5 = 10
15 - 10 = ?
5

Page 15
Write yes, 15, yes.

Pages 16-17
Circle 17, 25, 41, 34.
Color 66 ■, 70 ■, 92 ■

Page 18
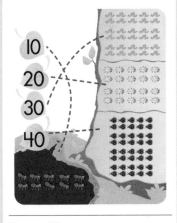

Page 19
Addition answers are 20, 60, 50.

Page 20
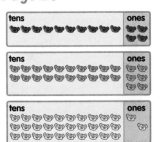

Page 21
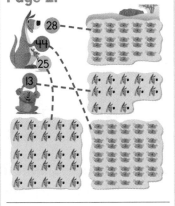

Page 22
Write 10, 10, 3, 23.

Page 23
21
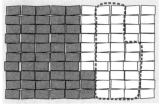

Page 24

Page 25
Write $15, $13, $12, $25.

Page 26
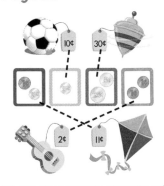

Page 27
Write 35¢, 8¢, 20¢, 22¢.

Page 28
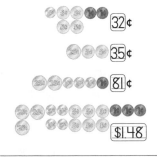

32¢
35¢
81¢
$1.48

Page 29

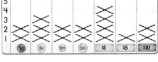

Page 30

Write 7, 7.

Page 31

Pages 32-33

Write 5, 4, 5, 7,3.
Color shapes

Page 34

Draw matching picture,
then **color**.

Page 35

Page 36

Color shapes

Page 37

Draw shapes to match.

Page 38

Write ▲▲ 8, ▬ 3, ● 6,
■ 6; triangles.

Page 39

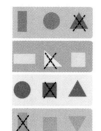

Page 40

Page 41

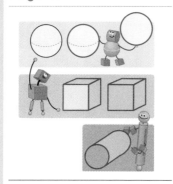

Page 42

Page 43

Page 44

Page 45

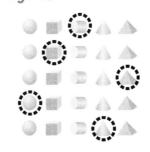

Page 46

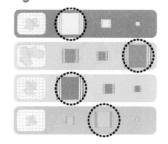

Page 47

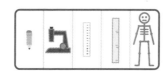

Page 48

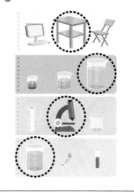

Page 49

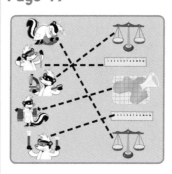

Page 50

 8, 4, 3, 6.

Page 51

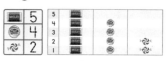

Page 52

Write 3, 2, 1.

Page 53

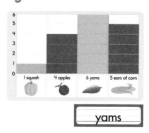

yams

Pages 54-55

Circle Saturday, 7,
Wednesday, 8, Thursday, 4.

Page 56

Circle 12, January, February,
June, 30, 2.

Page 57

Circle 31, 10.

Page 58

Child's answers will vary.
Here is an example.

7 o'clock   3 o'clock   8 o'clock

Page 59

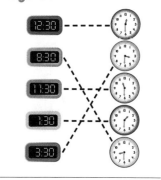

Page 60

7:30   2:30   6:00

You did it!

Create a cool sign to decorate your bedroom!

1. Cut on the – – – – line.
2. Fold on the – – – – line.
3. Carefully glue the sides together.
4. When the glue is dry, cut on the – – – – line.

Then, hang the sign on your doorknob!

®TREND

®TREND